THIS BOOK BELONGS TO:

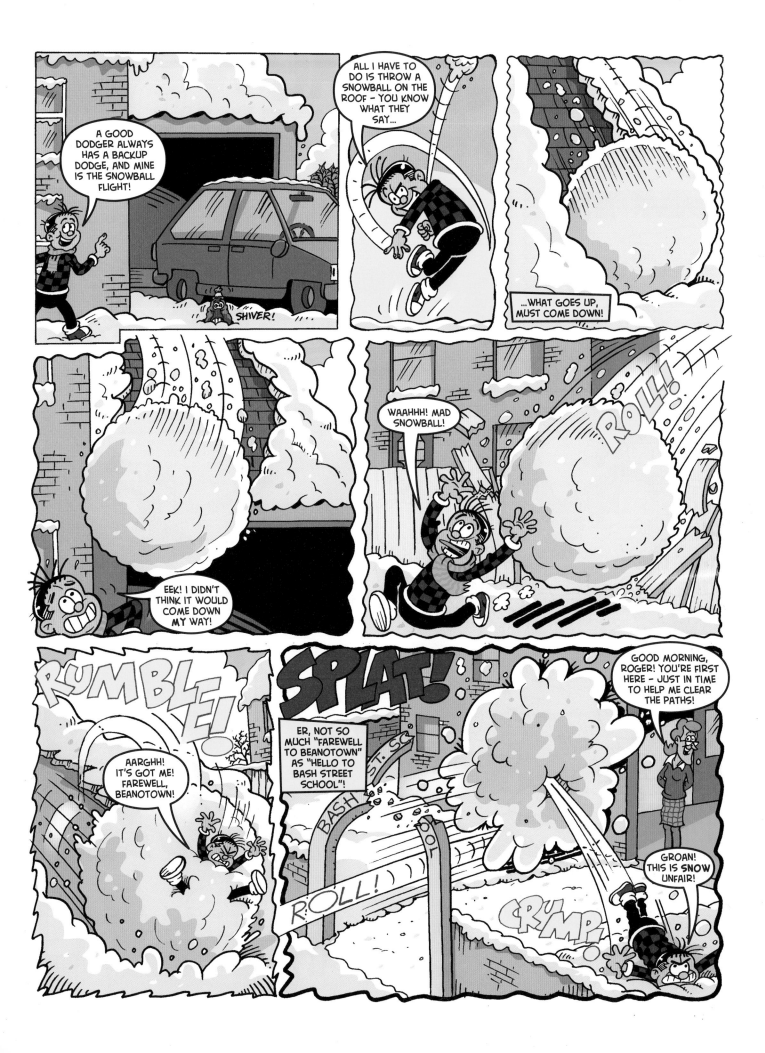

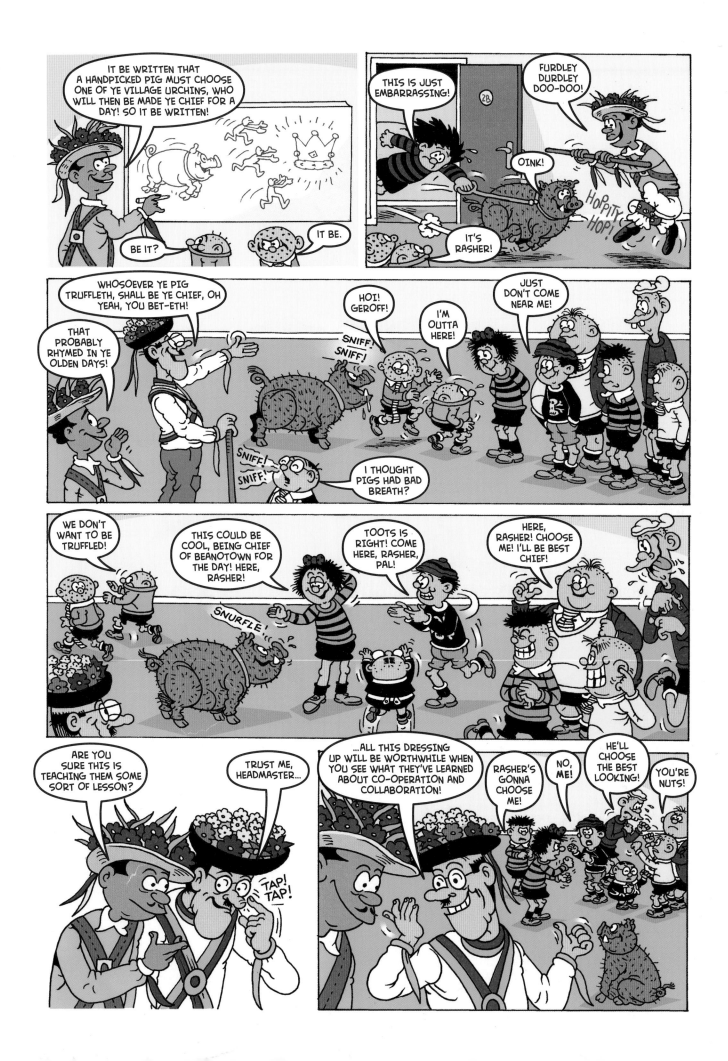

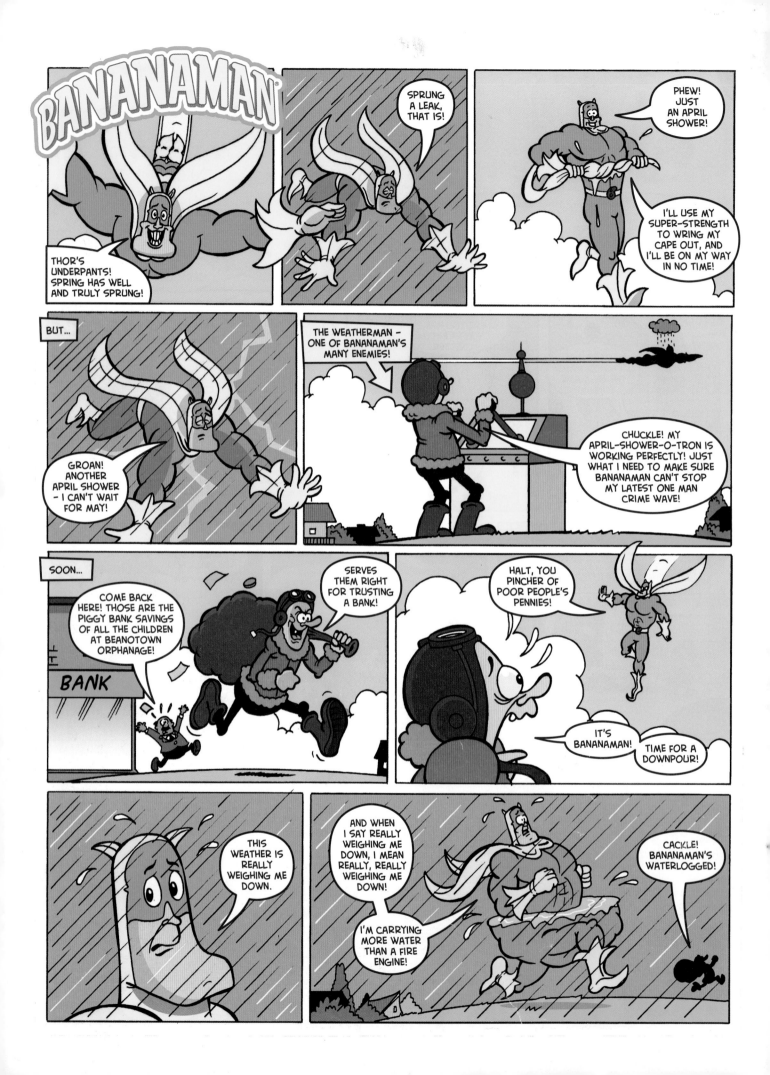

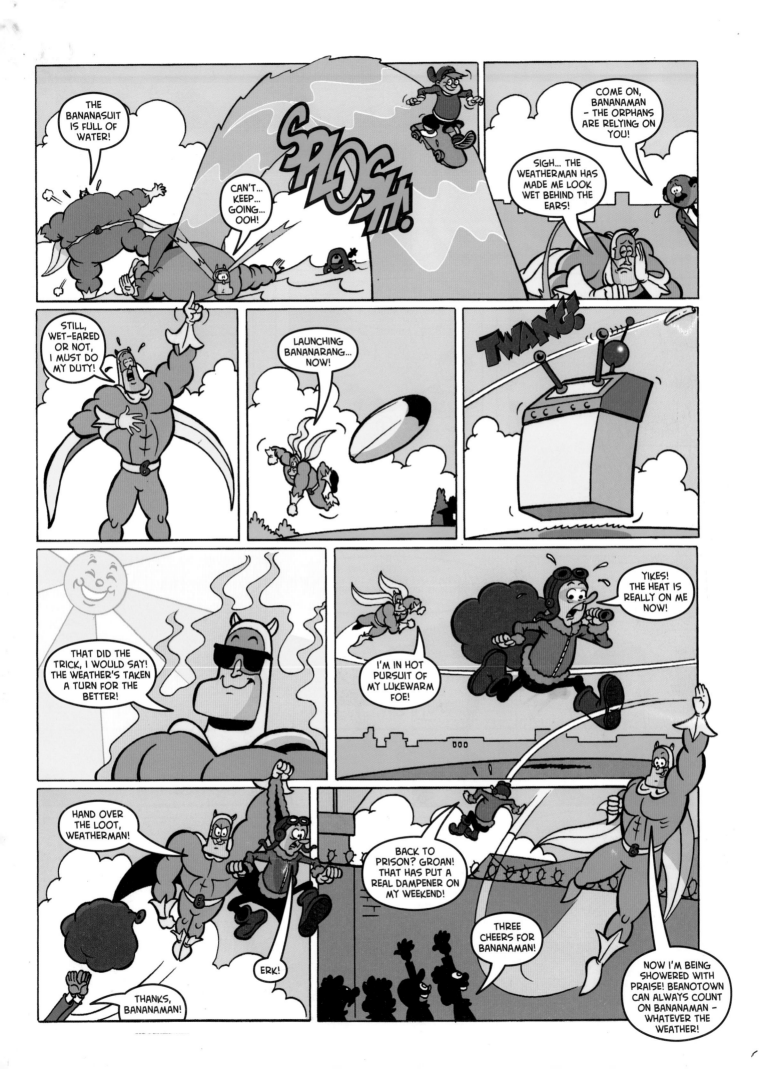

MAY THE FOURTH BE WITH YOU!

IT'S A DARK TIME FOR THE MENACE ALLIANCE. THE TEACHERS HAVE BROUGHT ORDER TO THE SCHOOL WITH THE HELP OF A SECRET TELL-TALE, THE IDENTITY OF WHICH NO-ONE KNOWS... OKAY, IT'S WALTER. OF COURSE IT'S WALTER, HE'S THE ONLY KID NOT IN DETENTION. IT'S A BIT OBVIOUS REALLY. ANYWAY, IT'S ALSO MAY THE FOURTH... YOU KNOW... STAR WARS DAY!

DENTENTION...

A TEACHER'S VOICE. CAN'T TELL WHICH - ED.

SIMMER DOWN!

EVERY KID IN SCHOOL'S IN DETENTION! WHAT ARE WE GONNA DO?

IT'S MAY THE FOURTH! STAR WARS DAY!

HOW DOES THAT HELP?

DUH! IT'S CALLED STAR WARS DAY BECAUSE IT'S THE ONE DAY OF THE YEAR THAT KIDS GET JEDI POWERS!

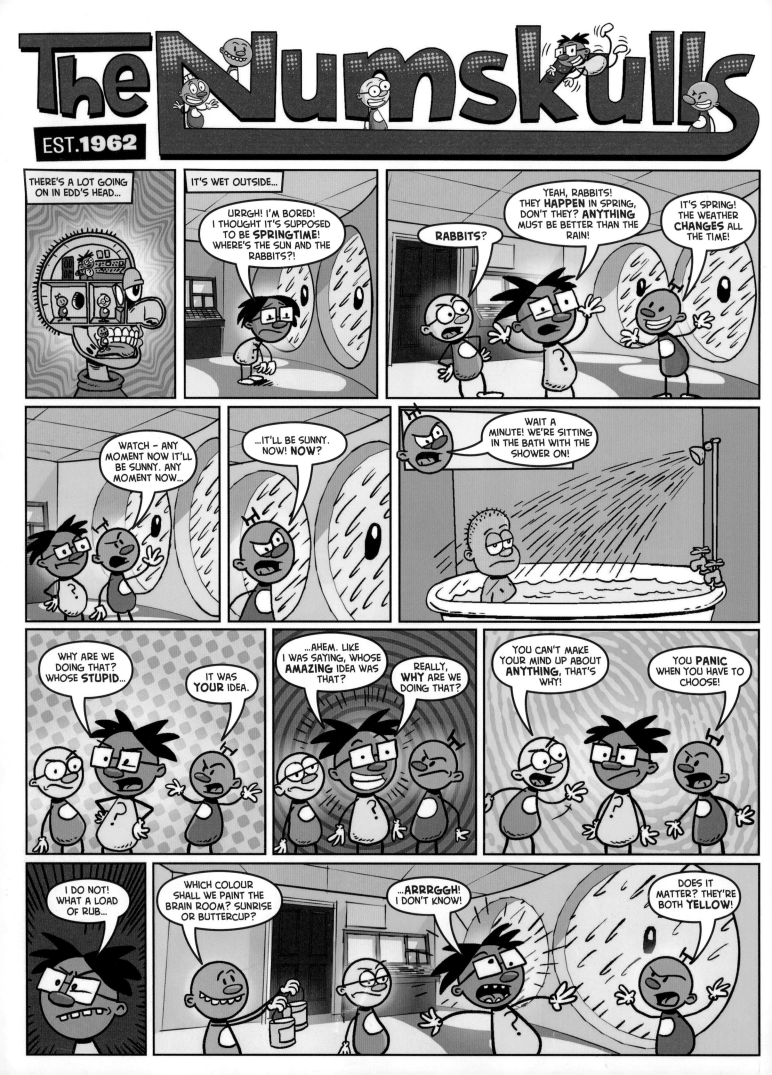

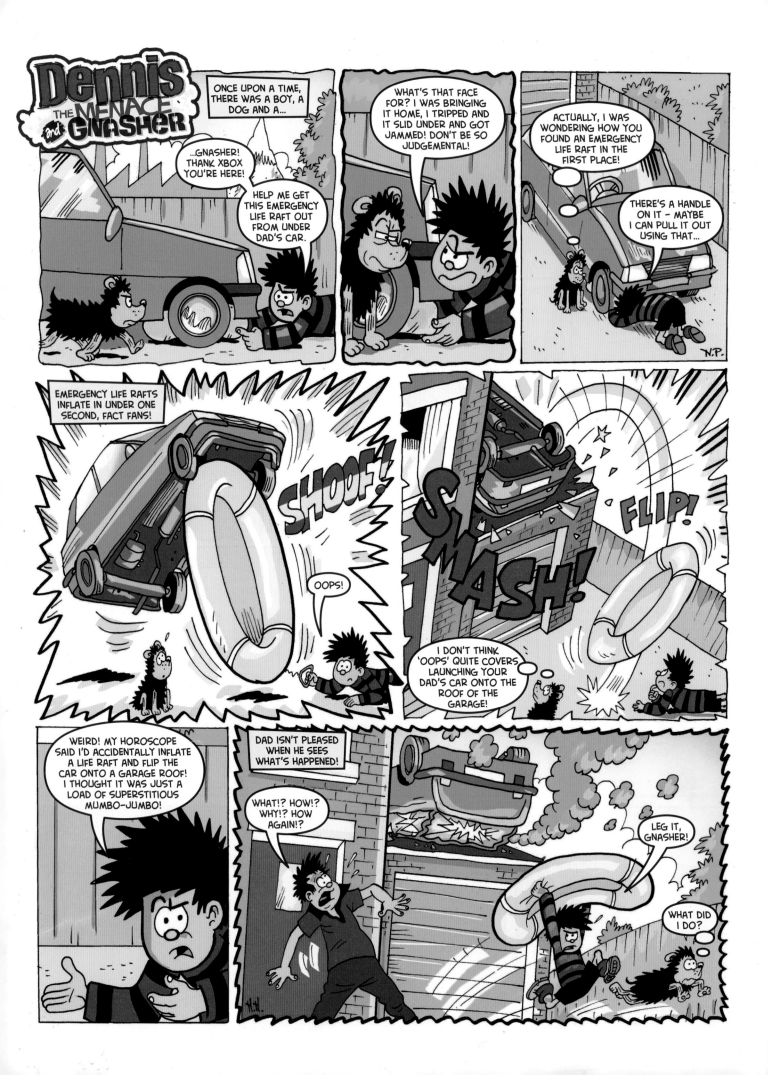

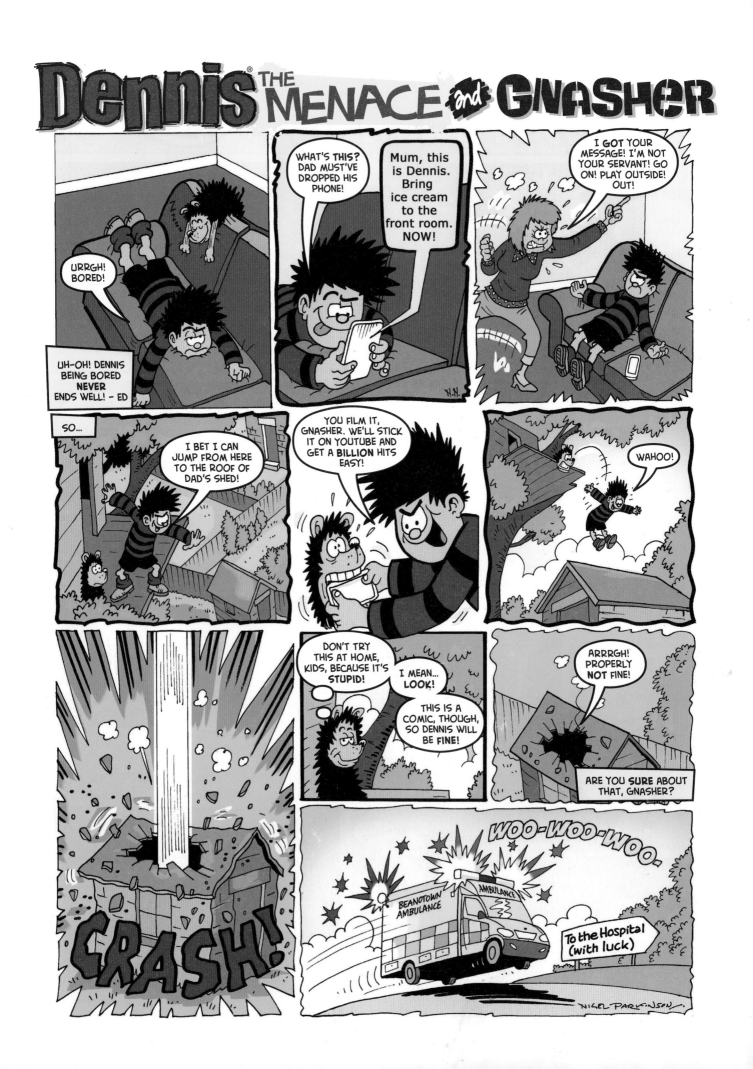

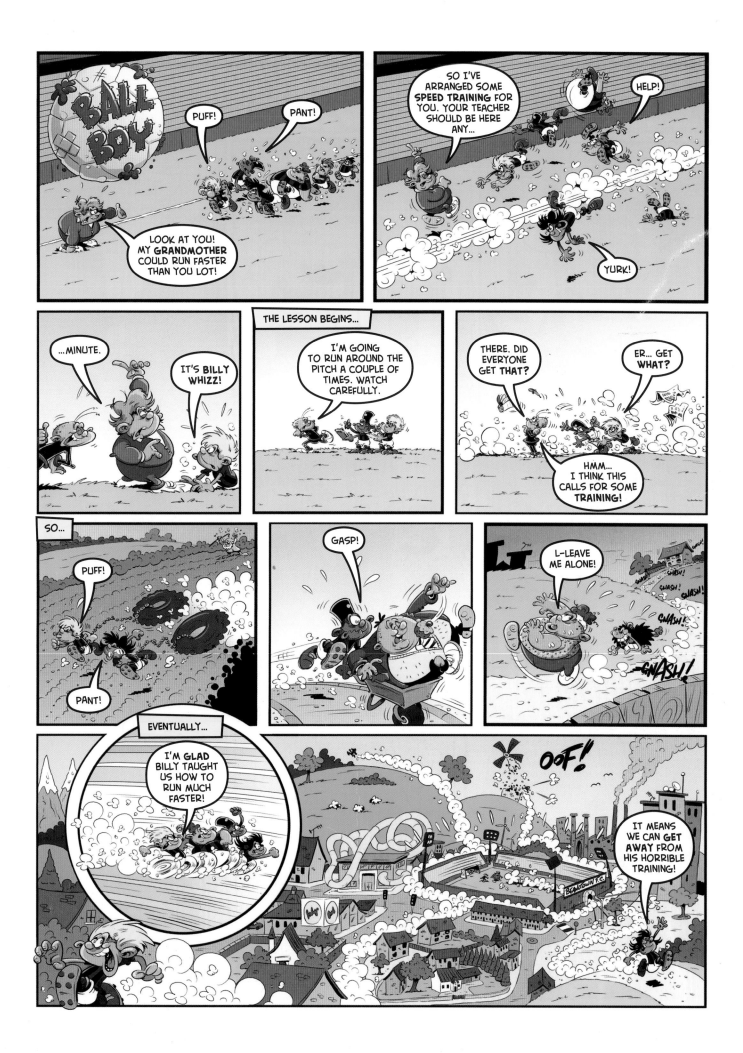

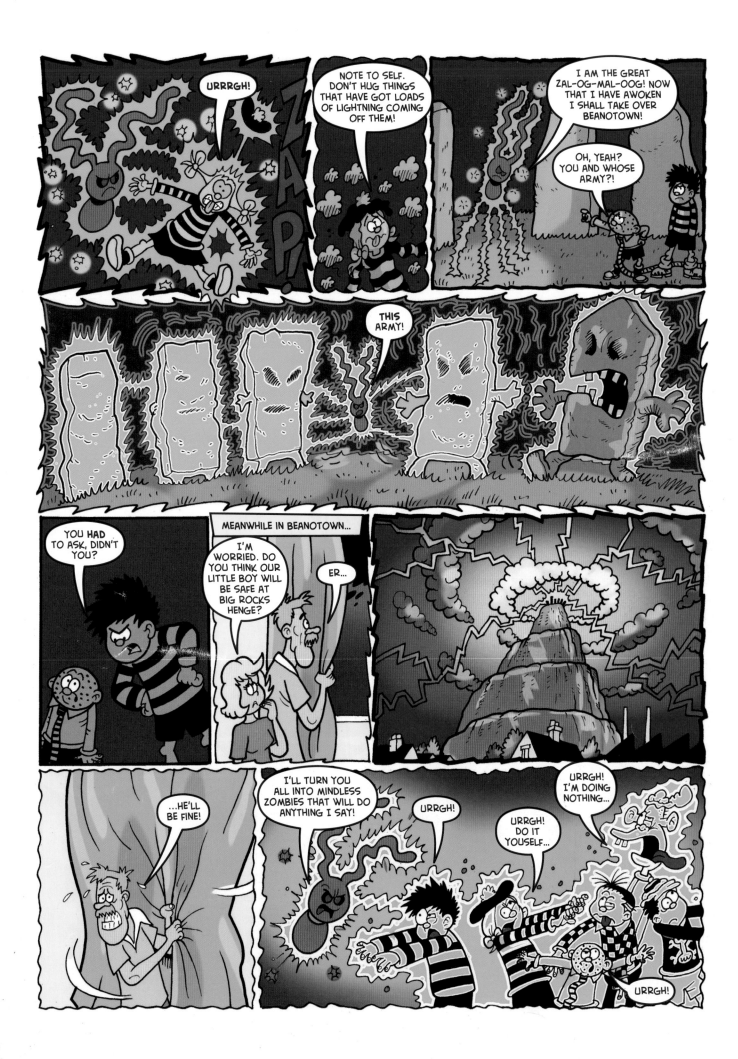

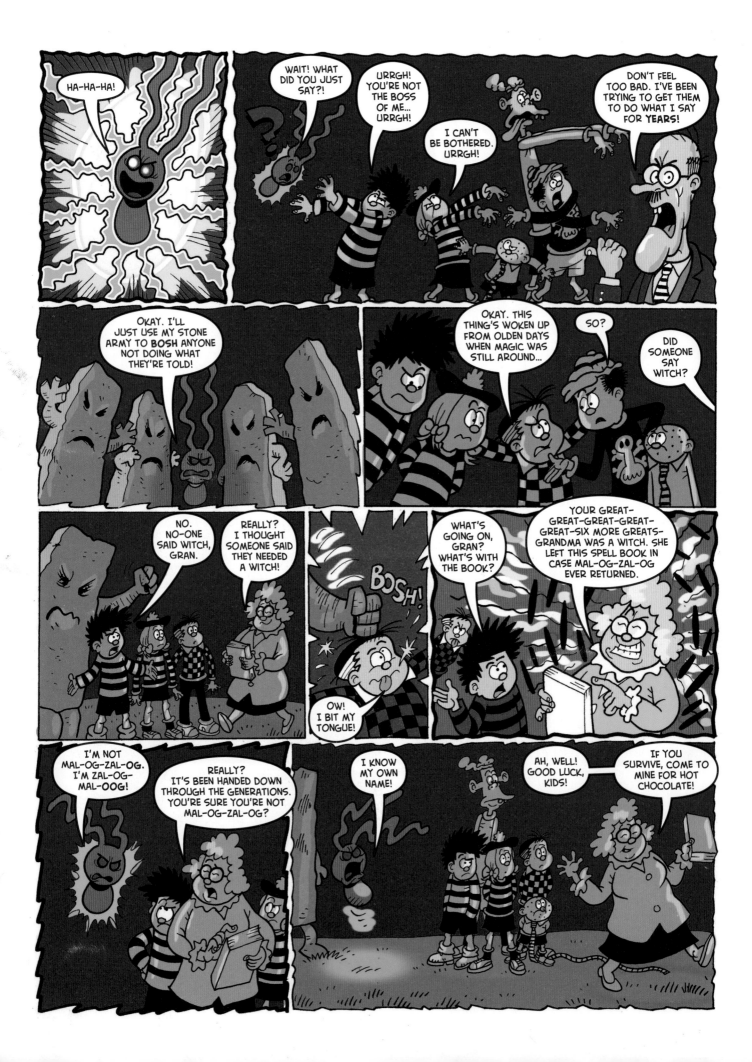

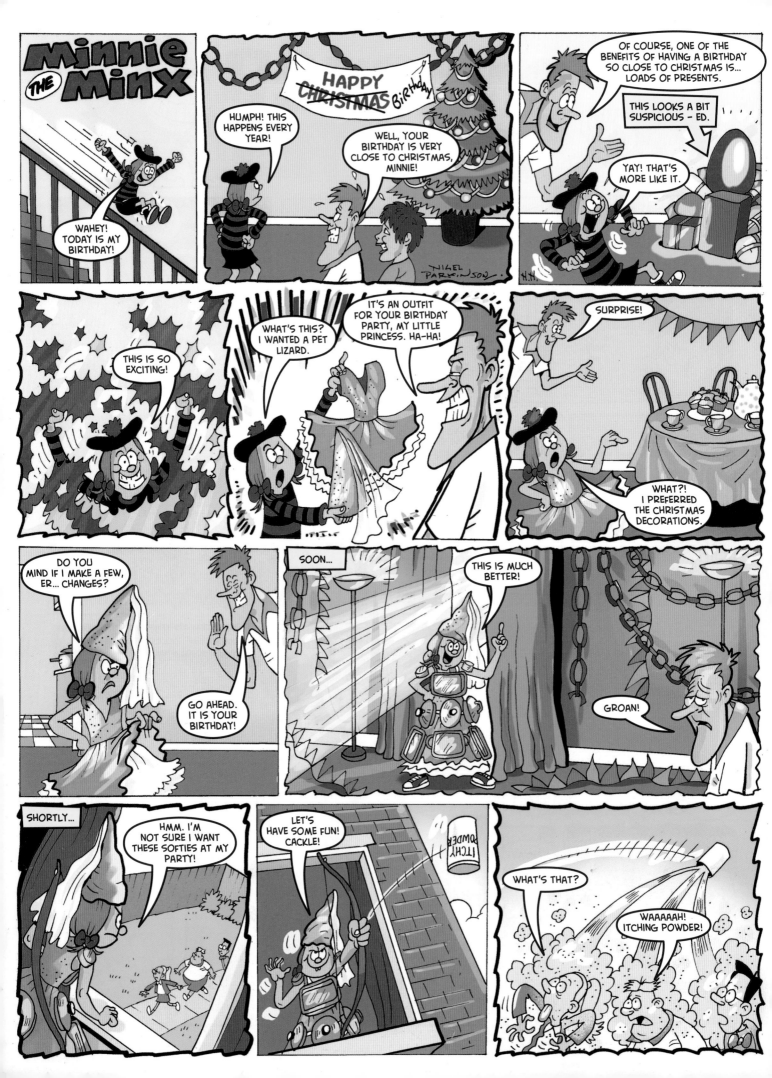

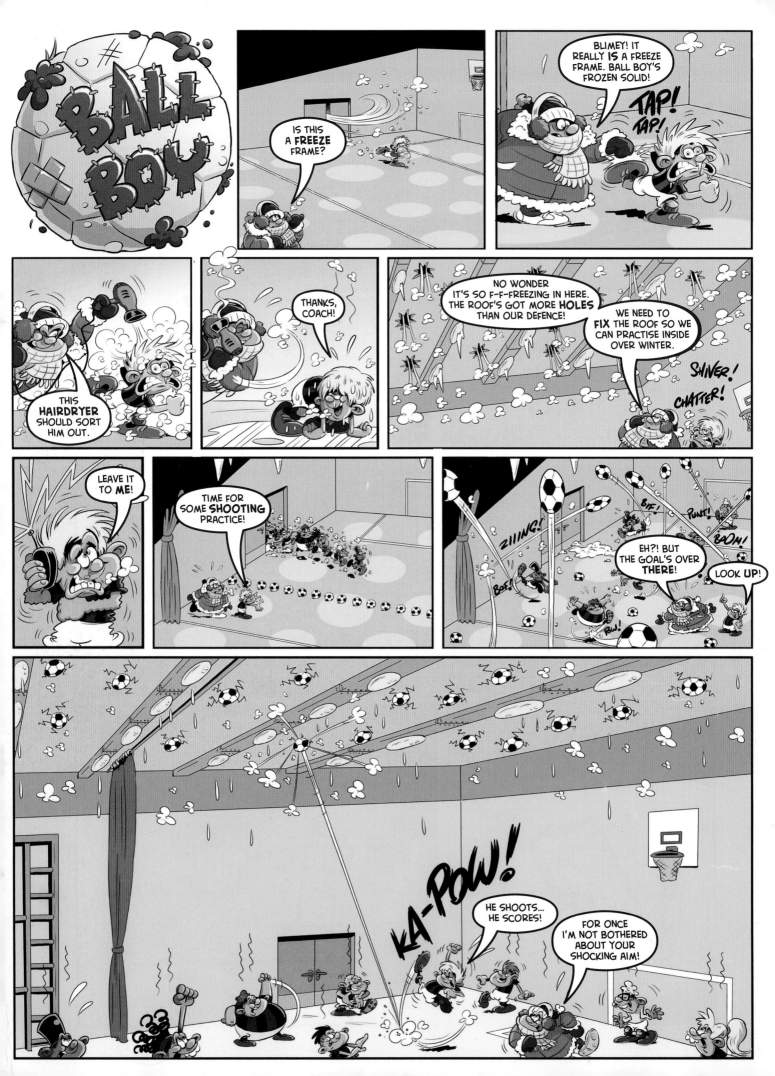